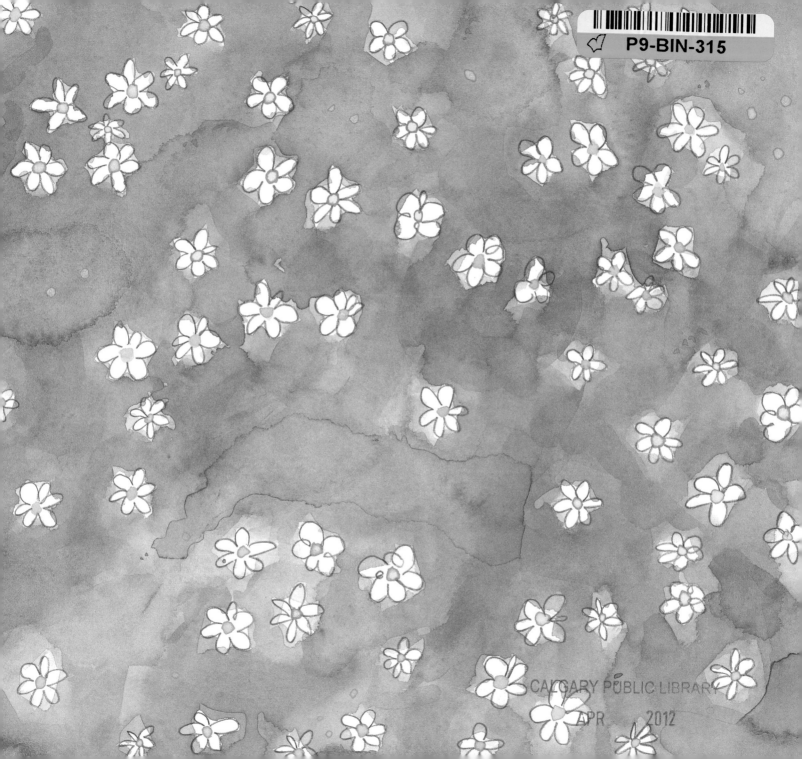

YOU

Stephen Michael King

Scholastic Canada Ltd.
Toronto New York London Auckland Sydney
Mexico City New Delhi Hong Kong Buenos Aires

Scholastic Canada Ltd.
604 King Street West, Toronto, Ontario M5V 1E1, Canada

Scholastic Inc.
557 Broadway, New York, NY 10012, USA

Scholastic Australia Pty Limited
PO Box 579, Gosford, NSW 2250, Australia

Scholastic New Zealand Limited
Private Bag 94407, Botany, Manukau 2163, New Zealand

Scholastic Children's Books
Euston House, 24 Eversholt Street, London NW1 1DB, UK

Typeset in Drawzing and Skissors.
Stephen Michael King created the illustrations using watercolour and ink.

Library and Archives Canada Cataloguing in Publication
King, Stephen Michael
You / Stephen Michael King.
ISBN 978-1-4431-0722-8 (bound). -- ISBN 978-1-4431-0723-5 (pbk.)
I. Title.
PZ7.K62Yo 2011   j823   C2010-906013-X

6 5 4 3 2 1   Printed in Singapore   46   11 12 13 14 15 16

The world is a colourful place.

Yellow,

red,

blue,

all colours.

Coloured with big things,

small things,

all sorts of things.

But the most colourful part of my world is . . .

you.

ting

The world is a musical place,

with high notes

and low notes,

all the notes in between.

Thump

Thoomp!

But the most musical part of my world is . . .

you.

The world is an exciting place,

with ups,

downs,

arounds and arounds,

and far-far-aways.

But the most exciting place in my world

is with . . .

you.